SPIRITUAL SELF-CARE

Workbook for Witches

A workbook designed to help you manage your wellness and mental health.

THOUGHT AWARENESS

Observe your stream of consciousness as you think about a stressful situation. Do not suppress any thoughts. Let them run their course while you watch them, and write them down as they occur.

Negative Thoughts

The next step is to rationally challenge the negative thoughts. Look at every thought you wrote down and ask yourself whether the thought is reasonable.

Rational Thoughts

Use rational, positive thoughts and affirmations to counter negative thinking. See if there are any opportunities that are offered by it.

Positive Thoughts

COGNITIVE RESTRUCTURING

Reducing Stress by Changing Your Thinking

Cognitive restructuring is useful for understanding what lies behind negative moods. These may undermine our performance, or damage our relationships with other people.

Step 1: Identify the Situation

Describe the situation that triggered your negative mood.

Step 2: Analyze Your Mood

Describe how you felt in the situation, and how you're feeling now.

Step 3: Identify Automatic Thoughts

Make a list of your automatic thoughts in response to the situation.

Step 4: Find Objective Evidence

Write down any evidence you can find that supports the automatic thoughts and any evidence that contradicts the thought.

Step 5: Monitor Your Present Mood

Take a moment to assess your mood. Do you feel better about the situation? Is there any action you need to take? Write down your present mood, along with any further steps that you need to take.

Understanding YOUR PROBLEMS

Try to fill in something of your own experience. You may begin to understand your difficulties a little better. Particularly what patterns may exist and how things interact.

Situation

Feelings

Thoughts

Physical Symptoms

Behaviors

Explain your spiritual beliefs.

Todays Mood: 

Why is self-care important?

Todays Mood:

Write down your self-care routine.

Todays Mood:

What big things are you most grateful for right now?

Todays Mood: 

What does spirituality mean to you?

Todays Mood: 

Where does your spirituality show up in your daily life?

Todays Mood: 

What makes the world a better place?

Todays Mood: 

Do you find your purpose or does your purpose find you?

Todays Mood: 

Do you believe you have a soul? Why?

Todays Mood: 

What is your intuition telling you right now?

Todays Mood: 

What ideas have had the biggest impact on your spiritual journey?

Todays Mood: 

What people have had the biggest impact on your spiritual journey?

Todays Mood: 

What's the number one problem you would like to solve in the world?

Todays Mood: 

What do you think happens when we die?

Todays Mood: 

Describe the witchy activities you do.

Todays Mood: 

When do you feel most powerful?

Todays Mood: 

When do you feel most connected to your spiritual side?

Todays Mood: 

What are some of the biggest unanswered questions in life?

Todays Mood: 

Describe your morning routine.

Todays Mood: 

How can you make your morning routine better?

Todays Mood: 

Describe your nighttime routine.

Todays Mood: 

How can you make your nighttime routine better?

Todays Mood: 

What do you want out of life?

Todays Mood: 

Make a list of your goals.

Todays Mood: 

Write about how you can accomplish your goals.

Todays Mood: 

What does it mean to embrace and accept your own darkness?

Todays Mood: 

What's preventing you from having the life you want?

Todays Mood: 

What traumatic event haven't you faced yet?

Todays Mood: 

How do you begin to heal?

Todays Mood: 

How does your trauma affect your everyday life?

Todays Mood: 

How can you make each day brighter?

Todays Mood: 

What popular opinion do you disagree with? Why?

Todays Mood: 

What is your favorite magical practice? Why?

Todays Mood: 

What are 10 things you have always felt deeply connected to?

Todays Mood: 

What is your spirit animal? What can you learn from this animal?

Todays Mood: 

Do you love yourself? How can you love yourself more?

Todays Mood: 

Do you fully appreciate your body? Talk about this.

Todays Mood: 

How are you treating your body?

Todays Mood: 

How can you treat your body better?

Todays Mood: 

Make your own ritual and write about the experience.

Todays Mood: 

Are you afraid of your own power? How can you embrace your power?

Todays Mood: 

How does your ego control you?

Todays Mood: 

Do you ignore your negative emotions?
Why?

Todays Mood: 

What element do you feel most connected to? Why?

Todays Mood: 

Go sit in nature. What do you notice?

Todays Mood: 

What can you learn from nature?

Todays Mood: 

How can you welcome more love and compassion into your life?

Todays Mood: 

Are you afraid to spend time alone? Why?

Todays Mood: 

Are your actions aligned with your values?
How can you create more alignment?

Todays Mood: 

What does being a witch mean to you?

Todays Mood: 

What are the little ways you judge yourself each day?

Todays Mood: 

How can you be less judgmental of yourself and others?

Todays Mood: 

Has practicing witchcraft changed your opinion on how the universe works? How?

Todays Mood: 

As a witch, what holidays do you celebrate and how do you celebrate them?

Todays Mood: 

Make a list of everything that makes you happy.

Todays Mood: 

What needs cleansing in your life?
How will you accomplish this?

Todays Mood: 

What makes you feel most alive?

Todays Mood: 

How is this year different from the others?

Todays Mood: 

How do you find peace in a chaotic world?

Todays Mood: 

What do you take for granted?

Todays Mood: 

What spiritual practices are beneficial for you? How do they help?

Todays Mood: 

Do you believe in a higher power? What does this mean for you?

Todays Mood: 

When was the last time you harmed someone?

Todays Mood: 

How can you avoid harming people in the future?

Todays Mood: 

Meditate and write about the experience.

Todays Mood: 

Write a letter to your inner child.

Todays Mood: 

How does spirituality help you through tough times?

Todays Mood: 

What have you learned about yourself in the past year?

Todays Mood: 

What's the connection between your soul and body?

Todays Mood: 

Describe how you feel when you pray or meditate.

Todays Mood: 

Do you ever compare yourself to others?
How can you stop this?

Todays Mood: 

What is your deepest fear? How will you overcome it?

Todays Mood: 

What faith or religion were you raised into? How do you feel about this?

Todays Mood: 

What does spiritual growth mean to you?

Todays Mood: 

How does the universe speak to you?

Todays Mood: 

Who or what is God to you?

Todays Mood: 

Who is your highest self and how do you connect with them?

Todays Mood: 

What blessings are you experiencing in life right now?

Todays Mood: 

Do you feel safe openly expressing spirituality? Why?

Todays Mood: 

When has the universe given you what you needed when you needed it?

Todays Mood: 

Are all humans connected? Talk about this.

Todays Mood: 

Do you trust your path or do you have a hard time releasing control? Talk about this.

Todays Mood: 

What about your spiritual self are you still discovering?

Todays Mood: 

How can you tell when your spiritual self has been neglected?

Todays Mood: 

How do you know the universe is always looking out for you?

Todays Mood: 

How does the higher power show up for you each day?

Todays Mood: 

Make a list of everything you love about yourself.

Todays Mood: 

What magical tools do you feel most drawn to? Why?

Todays Mood: 

What in life do you need help with?
What do you need? Who can you ask?

Todays Mood: 

What destructive habits do you need to let die? How will you do this?

Todays Mood: 

What rituals do you love to do?

Todays Mood: 

Write a letter to your shadow self.

Todays Mood: 

Is there something you're avoiding because of fear?

Todays Mood: 

Set a 10-minute timer and write everything that comes to your mind.

Todays Mood: 

How can you be true to yourself and live authentically each day?

Todays Mood: 

Made in the USA
Coppell, TX
13 June 2023

18023111R00056